.CLASSICS.
Illustrated®

William Shakespeare
A MIDSUMMER
NIGHT'S DREAM

essay by
Bruce Glassco Ph.D

ACCLAIM BOOKS
STUDY GUIDE

A Midsummer Night's Dream

art by Alex Blum

Classics Illustrated: *A Midsummer Night's Dream*
© Twin Circle Publishing Co.,
a division of Frawley Enterprises; licensed to First Classics, Inc.
All new material and compilation © 1997 by Acclaim Books, Inc.

Dale-Chall R.L.: 7.65

ISBN 1-57840-010-4

Acclaim Books, New York, NY
Printed in the United States

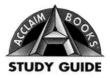

STUDY GUIDE

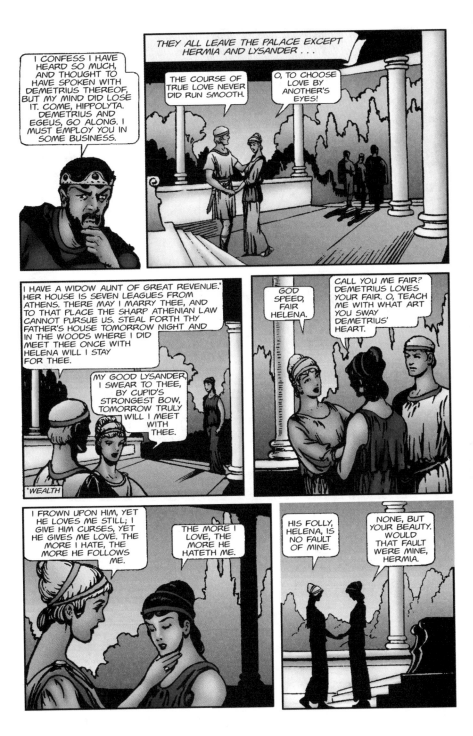

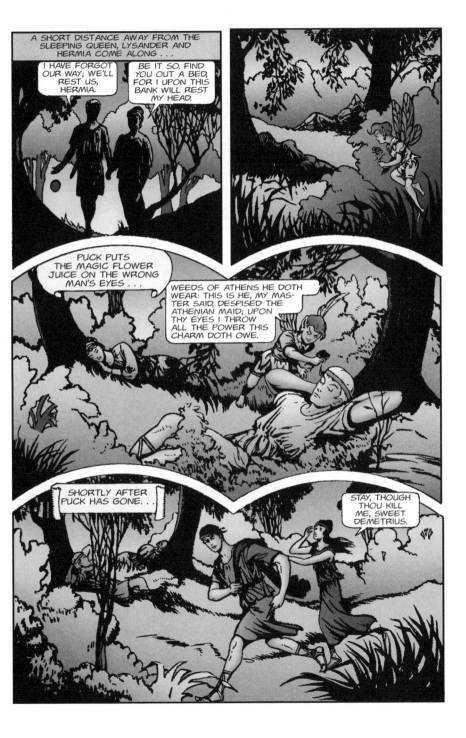

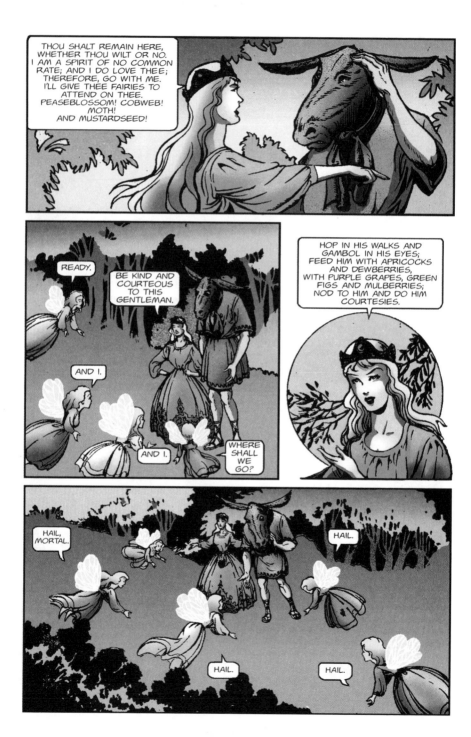

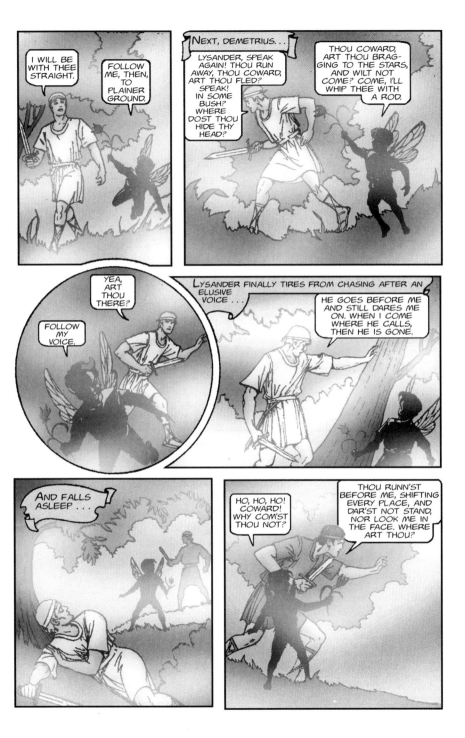

A MIDSUMMER NIGHT'S DREAM
WILLIAM SHAKESPEARE

There are those who insist someone other than Shakespeare wrote his famous plays, pointing out that, for such an illustrious playwright, Shakespeare left very little record of his passing. We have the plays themselves, of course—the large Folio volumes published after his death by his theatrical friends, and a few smaller Quartos published earlier. The preface to the folios includes a poem praising Shakespeare by his fellow playwright Ben Jonson, and an engraving of the writer's face; there's also a bust made not long after his death in Stratford on Avon. We have a half a dozen specimens of Shakespeare's handwriting, some official records, and a number of references to him by his contemporaries. Otherwise we are left with a lot of guesswork about this most famous of Elizabethans.

Still, it's hardly surprising that we know so little, considering how few records have managed to survive for four hundred years. Schoenbaum, one of Shakespeare's biographers, points out that we know even less about Shakespeare's friend Ben

Jonson, whose authorship no one has questioned; we don't know his birthplace or date, the name of his wife, or how many children he had. Compared to this, we have been able to uncover a good deal about the Bard of Avon.

William Shakespeare was born in 1564 in the small English town of Stratford-on-Avon. His father, John Shakespeare, made gloves for a living, and it's possible that he never learned to write. At one time he rose to the position of High Bailiff, the equivalent of Mayor, but by the time William was a teenager, he had fallen on hard times—perhaps due to lawsuits or personal enemies. Still, it's unlikely that the family was ever actually poor as the young poet grew.

Shakespeare attended the local Stratford grammar school, and as far as we know that is the extent of his formal education. This limitation has been used by those who argue that someone else wrote the plays; how could a country school have given Shakespeare the education which is evident in every line of his work? We should remember that Elizabethan schools expected far more from their students than ours do today. He certainly would have studied classical languages and literature—and what Ben Jonson sneeringly referred to as "little Latin and less Greek" would still be impressive by today's standards.

At eighteen, Shakespeare married. Anne Hathaway was seven or eight years older than he, and already several months pregnant at the time of the wedding. Was it a shotgun wedding? We don't know, nor do we know much about the bride herself. All we know is that the marriage produced three children, Susanna in 1583 and the twins Hamnet and Judith in 1585. Hamnet was apparently named after a neighbor, not the Danish prince of his father's play. The boy died at thirteen years of age, but the two girls lived to marry and have children. Apparently Shakespeare left his family behind in Stratford during his years as a London playwright.

We know almost nothing about Shakespeare's life for the ten years after his marriage, except that he went to London and become involved with the theater. The young man must have had an intense love of the stage to draw him from the security of Stratford into the uncertain life of an actor. Probably such a theatre company came through Stratford when Shakespeare was young, touring to escape the hot, plague-ridden summers in London; could that have inspired a life-long passion in the glovemaker's son? Perhaps he got

his start as an actor playing female roles (an area usually reserved for the youngest members of a company), since by law only men were allowed to appear on stage. When Shakespeare was thirty-one he was listed as a member of the Lord Chamberlain's men, a relatively distinguished company of actors with which he was associated for the rest of his life. The name came from the fact that, like most acting companies, they had a wealthy patron to help pay the bills. When King James I took the throne in 1603, he adopted Shakespeare's troupe as the King's Men, perhaps indicating their pre-eminence in the theatrical world.

The decades of the 1590s and 1600s were the years of Shakespeare's greatest works. He wrote over thirty-five comedies, tragedies, and histories, and was evidently one of the leading managers of the company. During this period he prospered, gaining shares in the Globe and Blackfriars theaters and buying property back in Stratford.

Eventually, for whatever reason, he decided that he'd had enough. By around 1612, he had returned to Stratford, where he remained for the rest of his life, making occasional trips to London to oversee his investments or, in one case, to collaborate on the play *Henry VIII*. In 1616, at the age of fifty-two, Shakespeare died.

A verse above his grave in the church where he is buried reads:

Good friend for Jesus' sake forebear,
To dig the dust enclosèd here!
Blessed be the man that spares these stones,
And cursed be he that moves my bones.

This threat is probably the only thing that could have kept four centuries' worth of scholars and enthusiasts from excavating to retrieve clues and souvenirs, to test pet theories, or to enshrine the playwright's remains in Westminster Abbey beside Chaucer, Spenser, and the others in Poet's Corner.

What was Shakespeare like? The comments we have from his con-

Who Wrote Shakespeare's Plays?

Many scholars have been frustrated by the lack of information about Shakespeare's life. Shouldn't such a great writer, they wonder, have left more of a mark on his own time? Other readers are bothered by Shakespeare's humble origins. Never mind that many other celebrated geniuses—John Keats, Leonardo da Vinci, Albert Einstein—also had no relation to aristocracy. Some of these readers became convinced that the learning and refinement displayed in the plays were beyond the reach of a tradesman's son from the small town of Stratford. They wanted an author of heroic stature, and they searched until they uncovered one—or several.

Speculation as to the plays' true authorship centered during the nineteenth century on Sir Francis Bacon, a noted essayist and scientific inquirer who would seem to be temperamentally unsuited for Shakespeare's flights of fancy. Some of his adherents even argued that, in his spare time, he was responsible not only for all Shakespeare's plays but for the works of Spenser, Burton, Marlowe, and any number of other Elizabethan writers. A more recent candidate has been Edward de Vere, seventeenth Earl of Oxford, despite

his death several years before the production of several of Shakespeare's major plays. Playwright Christopher Marlowe was murdered before Shakespeare began to write—unless, as some of his adherents argue, the death was faked. And the list goes on and on: Sir Walter Raleigh, Sir Philip Sidney, Cardinal Wolsey, the Earl of Essex, the Earl of Southampton, a consortium of Jesuits, Shakespeare's wife Anne Hathaway, even Queen Elizabeth and King James I.

Fans of these theories often spend a lifetime of work and fortunes investigating their claims. They often resort to elaborate, fanciful cryptography schemes, as if whoever wrote the plays was more interested in encoding complex hidden messages than in producing meaningful drama or beautiful poetry. They tend to approach the plays as a detective approaches a crime, with little appreciation for either literature or history. Sadly, even a few otherwise brilliant individuals, including Mark Twain, Henry James, and Sigmund Freud, have been taken in by anti-Stratfordian beliefs. Among reputable scholars, however, the authorship of the Shakespeare canon has never been held in serious doubt.

temporaries are usually flattering, but there's little indication that he was recognized during his lifetime as being one of England's greatest writers. Compared to contemporaries like the flamboyant Christopher Marlowe, who possibly worked as a spy and eventually was killed in a tavern brawl, or the outgoing Ben Jonson, he seems to have been a relatively quiet man. His theatrical friends say that he wrote smoothly and easily, with never "a blot in his papers." From the attention he paid to their publication, he seems to have thought more highly of his sonnets and longer poems than of his plays. Perhaps he wrote the plays quickly, to meet deadlines. He was certainly intimately familiar with the theatre, and what does and doesn't work on stage. Even today, the best way to experience his work is unquestionably to see it on stage or screen.

Midsummer Night's Dream was written in 1595, when Shakespeare was just beginning to hit his stride. Farces like *Comedy of Errors* and lesser tragedies like *Romeo and Juliet* lay behind him; most of his great tragedies and histories were

The World of the Dream

Most of Shakespeare's plays are set in one of three major locales. His histories take place in Great Britain, from the fourteenth century to Shakespeare's recent past. Many of his tragedies and comedies have continental locations, often a rather vague Italy.

Midsummer Night's Dream is one of the plays, along with *Julius Caesar* and *Pericles*, set in classical times. There was considerable interest in the days of Greece and Rome in Shakespeare's time; indeed, the term "Renaissance" comes from the idea of a "rebirth" of the glories of antiquity. However, the Athens described in this play is nothing that a scholar of antiquity would recognize.

When Theseus threatens to make Hermia "abjure forever the society of men" (Act I, Sc. 1) by forcing her into a nunnery, he alludes somewhat vaguely to "Diane's altar," but it seems clear that Shakespeare is thinking of a sixteenth-century nunnery, not an ancient Greek institution. Shakespeare's "hempen homespuns" are exactly the same working-class men who would have made up the groundlings of Shakespeare's audience.

It's also unlikely that the play as it was originally performed would have had any attempt at period staging. The theatrical managers had spent a good deal of money on the finest clothes currently available, and they would expect their actors to wear them whether portraying a fourteenth-century monarch like Richard II, a Roman like Julius Caesar, or an ancient Briton like King Lear.

still to come. Some have called it his first mature play, when he finally felt at ease and confident with his own abilities. There's a tradition that the play was originally written and performed, not for the London stage, but rather as special entertainment for a private wedding ceremony. It's interesting to speculate how it might have been received by its original aristocratic audience.

The Plot and Players

An important thing to remember about Shakespeare's theatre is that he wrote for several different audiences at the same time. If you went to see a play in the Globe Theatre, you would see three tiers of seats around the outside of the "wooden O," where the audience paid two or three pennies to sit in relative comfort.

On the Globe's ground level were the people who couldn't afford to pay more than the basic entrance fee—usually a penny. These were called the groundlings. There weren't any seats in this section, so they had to stand or walk around. If they got bored, they might start conversations with each other, or call out encouragement or heckling to the actors on stage. When an Elizabethan theatre was excavated recently, whole layers of ground-up chestnut shells were discovered. So there must have been people selling nuts right in the theatre, and probably oranges and other fruit as well. Actors must have needed pretty good lungs to talk over the cracking of nuts and buzz of conversation in a roofless, open-air theatre!

Shakespeare's company also occasionally did performances for special occasions at the estates and palaces of the nobility. In the later years of Shakespeare's life, they purchased a building which they turned into a new kind of indoor theatre, with seating for everyone and artificial lighting, which was meant to appeal to a more aristocratic audience. This was called the Blackfriars Theatre.

With all of these different audiences, Shakespeare needed to write plays that would appeal to both the highly educated nobility and the common groundlings. Many of his plays, therefore, especially his comedies, have two separate plots: one full of noble people doing noble things, and one full of everyday people who get in comically ridiculous situations. Other contemporary playwrights did the same thing, but Shakespeare was a master at tying the different plots together thematically. In Henry IV, for example, Prince Hal has to choose between the life of the earthy Falstaff and his low-class friends, or the life of a prince represented by the rash, high-minded Hotspur.

A Midsummer Night's Dream may have originally been written to be performed at a nobleman's wedding, rather than in one of the big theatres. Nevertheless, Shakespeare certainly filled it with characters who would appeal to groundlings as well as to the nobility. The play has not two, but three separate plots, all brilliantly tied together by the character of Puck. It may help to understand the play if we discuss each of the three parts separately.

Shakespeare was not the first author to point out how much of our lives seems determined by forces beyond our control. His source material, the ancient Greek Dionysian plays, often centered around the struggles between gods and goddesses, and the effects these conflicts had on the destinies of unwitting mortals. *The Iliad*, the great Greek epic of the Trojan War, tells us the entire conflict arose from a quarrel between goddesses about which of them was the most beautiful. Mortals' lives are frequently blighted by the unrelenting enmity of a god or goddess, or aided by a deity who takes a particular interest in them.

The omnipotent splendor of the Greek gods and goddesses was too heavy-handed for what Shakespeare had in mind for this play. Instead, for the machinery that made his plot engine run, he hit upon the idea of using the folk tradition of fairies.

There's still something of the god, though, in the way Oberon manipulates the affairs of mortals behind the scenes. Several of Shakespeare's comedies have this sort of powerful, secretive, benevolent figure working undercover to make everything come out all right: Duke Vincentio in *Measure for Measure* or Prospero in *The Tempest*. Unlike those plays, however, the other characters in *Midsummer Night's Dream* never manage to figure out what is going on—only Oberon, Puck, and we in the audience know the full story. Fairies have been a part of world folklore from time immemorial. Some theories hold that they are dim survivors of the myths of pagan gods (the moon goddess Diana was accompanied by a troop of foresters and hunters, and these may have metamorphosed into our concept of fairies). In England the idea of the "Little People" may have come from the remnants of the ancient Britons, driven underground when their country was conquered by the Saxons. Sometimes in folklore the fairies are as small as insects, sometimes just short, and sometimes human or larger; Shakespeare does nothing to sort out the confusion—Oberon and Titania seem to be regular humans in size, but Bottom says to one of Titania's fairies, "Mounsieur Cobweb, good mounsieur, get you your weapons in your hand, and kill me a red-hipped humble-bee on the top of a thistle" (*Act IV, Sc.1.*).

When we meet them at the begin-

TAKE SOME OF IT, AND SEEK THROUGH THIS GROVE A SWEET ATHENIAN IN LOVE WITH A DISDAINFUL YOUTH. ANOINT HIS EYES.

ning of Act II, Titania and Oberon are having a quarrel. Both of them want possession of the same thing: a changeling, an orphaned human child who is being raised among the fairies. When Titania refuses to give Oberon the boy, the fairy king begins to plot revenge. By embarrassing and distracting her, he hopes, he can make her give the child to him.

FOR OBERON IS WRATH BECAUSE SHE, AS HER ATTENDANT, HATH A LOVELY BOY STOLEN FROM AN INDIAN KING; AND JEALOUS OBERON WOULD HAVE THE CHILD, BUT SHE WITHHOLDS THE LOVED BOY.

To help him with his revenge he calls his assistant, Puck. Puck comes from a long lineage of trickster beings. The name comes from the Persian word Pouka, a kind of invisible spirit. In England he was called Robin Goodfellow for the same reason that the fairies were called the Good Folk, or in ancient Greece the Furies were called the Kindly Ones—with the hope that, if you referred to them politely, these dangerous creatures might leave you alone. The tradition of the hobgoblin arose among peasants who needed some explanation for why the milk sometimes curdled, or why you could put something down and

then not find it ten minutes later.

Puck's life consists of an unending series of practical jokes, which he describes in the beginning of Act II: he uses his shapechanging ability to become a roasted crab in a bowl of soup, so that he can spill it in someone's lap, or transforms himself into a three-legged stool, and slips out from underneath people just as they are about to sit down. It comes as no surprise, then, that when Oberon wants revenge on his queen, it is to Puck he turns. He tells his servant to go find a particular flower, called "Love-in-Idleness." "The juice of it," he explains, "on sleeping eyelids laid, will make or man or woman madly

FETCH ME THAT FLOWER; THE HERB I SHOWED THEE ONCE; THE JUICE OF IT ON SLEEPING EYELIDS LAID WILL MAKE MAN OR WOMAN MADLY DOTE UPON THE NEXT LIVE CREATURE THAT IT SEES. FETCH ME THAT HERB; AND BE THOU HERE AGAIN ERE THE LEVIATHAN' CAN SWIM A LEAGUE.

I'LL PUT A GIRDLE ROUND THE EARTH IN FORTY MINUTES.

'WHALE

dote upon the next live creature that it sees." He'll make her fall in love with something amusing, "lion, bear or wolf, or bull, or meddling monkey, or on busy ape," and in her besotted condition she will give him the child he has been seeking.

To us, Oberon seems a vindictive, even a rather abusive husband. Perhaps in this Shakespeare is again following the lead of the ancient Greeks, whose great gods Zeus and Hera were subject to jealous squabbles.

The Rustics

Another major subplot involves the lower classes—supposedly Athenian tradesmen, but actually drawn from the rank and file of the London workers in Shakespeare's audience. People who write about the play refer to these characters in various ways: rustics (meaning uneducated country people), or mechanicals (people who work with their hands), or even "rusty mechanics." Every other character in the play speaks verse, either rhymed or unrhymed iambic pentameter, but these characters all speak common prose.

They are: Tom Snout, a tinker (one who mends broken pots and other appliances); Robin Starveling, a tailor; Francis Flute, a bellows-mender; Peter Quince, a carpenter; Snug. a joiner (a carpenter who makes furniture); and, most importantly, Nick Bottom, a weaver.

The rustics have gathered together to put on a play, which they hope to present to Theseus, the Duke of Athens, on his wedding-day. This play-within-a-play is an old story that would have been familiar to Shakespeare's audience. Briefly: Pyramus and Thisbe are neighbors who are in love, but as with Romeo and Juliet or Hermia and Lysander, their parents won't allow them to be married. They talk through a chink in the wall between their houses, and agree to meet outside the city at night. Thisbe arrives first, but is frightened by a lion and runs away, though not before the lion has mauled her mantle with its bloody mouth. Then Pyramus arrives, finds the bloody mantle, and promptly commits suicide. Thisbe comes back, finds her dead lover, and kills herself with his sword. Shakespeare had already given a similar story a serious treatment in *Romeo and Juliet*; now, a year later, he pointed out the plot's absurdity.

Even before the rustics begin rehearsals, a problem develops. In one of the funniest scenes in the play, it turns out that Bottom turns out to be a shameless ham. He wants to play the part of the hero, the heroine, even the lion; the director, Peter Quince, is hard-pressed to know what to do with him.

In this scene Shakespeare is drawing on a tradition that would have been well-known to his audience: the phenomenon of the tradesman-actor. Drama got its start in Great Britain in the Middle Ages largely through the trade guilds. At yearly festivals in the towns, the guilds would meet and compete with one another to produce the largest and most spectacular production. These were of two types: one, the mystery play, dealt with events in the Bible, and the other, the morality play, dealt with allegorical treatments of good and evil. Just because the plays were religious in nature doesn't mean they weren't funny. The role of Herod in the Christmas story, for instance, was usually played by the biggest ham actor in town, who would bellow and bluster and generally carry on. Shakespeare is making fun these amateur actors with the characters of Bottom and his friends, but he is doing so gently. Bottom is ridiculous, but his heart is in the right place.

The rustics decide to go out of town and rehearse at night, in the forest, so that no one will see them practice. However, almost as soon as they begin, Puck wanders by. Never one to pass by the opportunity for a practical joke, he waits until Bottom goes off-stage, and then invisibly makes his move. When Bottom emerges again, his own head has been replaced by the head of a donkey. Needless to say, the other tradesmen are terrified and take to their heels, and Puck helps to chase them away.

When Titania, Queen of the Fairies, wakes up from her nap, the first thing she sees, with her eyes streaked with the juice of Oberon's flower, is Bottom wearing his donkey head. Puck has brought about exactly the kind of ridiculous situation that Oberon hoped for, and Titania immediately falls in love with the oafish rustic. She gives commands to her attendant fairies to wait on the mortal, and leads him to her bower. Along the way she meets Oberon, and finally gives him the changeling child he had wanted. In gratitude, once she has fallen asleep Oberon uses another flower to undo the charm of the first one. When she awakens and sees the hairy head lying beside her, she can scarcely believe her eyes, but Oberon explains and, evidently, the couple are reconciled.

In the morning, Bottom wakes up and goes back into the city, where his friends are overjoyed to see him with his own head once again. They put on their play for Duke Theseus and the other characters, and it turns out to be unintentionally hilarious. At the end, Bottom stages one of the most elaborate and over-acted death scenes in all of literature.

SINCE LION VILE HATH DEFLOWERED MY DEAR, I DIE THUS, NOW I AM DEAD.

The situation with the lovers is one of the funniest parts of the play, but also one of the most confusing. It may help to draw diagrams to explain what is going on.

At the beginning of the play, Hermia and Lysander are in love, but Hermia's father, Egeus, is opposed to their marriage. He wants her to marry another man, Demetrius. We also find out that Demetrius had once courted another woman, Helena, who still loves him, but that he had abandoned her to pursue Hermia. The diagram of their affections at this stage would look like this:

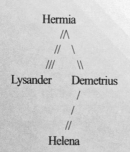

I HAVE A WIDOW AUNT OF GREAT REVENUE.' HER HOUSE IS SEVEN LEAGUES FROM ATHENS. THERE MAY I MARRY THEE, AND TO THAT PLACE THE SHARP ATHENIAN LAW CANNOT PURSUE US. STEAL FORTH THY FATHER'S HOUSE TOMORROW NIGHT AND IN THE WOODS WHERE I DID MEET THEE ONCE WITH HELENA WILL I STAY FOR THEE.

MY GOOD LYSANDER, I SWEAR TO THEE, BY CUPID'S STRONGEST BOW, TOMORROW TRULY WILL I MEET WITH THEE.

'WEALTH'

```
                Hermia
                 /\
                // \
               ///  \\
        Lysander    Demetrius
                     /
                    /
                   //
                Helena
```

So far, this looks like a fairly standard beginning for a romance; in fact, it's pretty similar to the beginning of *Romeo and Juliet*, which Shakespeare had written the previous year. The subsequent developments are also fairly standard for stories of this sort. Theseus, the Duke of Athens, tells Hermia that she must either marry the man her father has chosen, or live the rest of her life as a nun, or be put to death. Faced with these choices, she and Lysander decide instead to sneak out into the forest in the middle of the night, and elope. They tell their plans to Hermia's friend Helena, and Helena in turn tells her love, Demetrius. She does this mostly so that, when he pursues his rival Lysander into the forest, she can follow and be alone with the object of her hopeless affection.

It's when they arrive in the forest that things get…interesting. Oberon, waiting for Puck to bring him the flower that creates love, sees Demetrius scorn Helena when she pursues him through the forest. Puck returns with the flower, and Oberon gives him some of its buds, telling his servant to find the Athenian gentleman and put some of the flower's juice into his eyes.

Of course, a plan like this is bound to go wrong. First of all, Oberon doesn't know that there are two Athenian men in the forest. Second, Puck enjoys nothing more than a practical joke: instead of finding Demetrius, Puck puts the juice of the flower onto Lysander's eyes. Of course, when he wakes up, the first person he sees is Helena, who happens to be wandering by, and he immediately abandons his former love (Hermia) to run after Helena.

The diagram of affection now looks like this:

```
            Hermia
             /\
            /  \
           \/   \
     Lysander   Demetrius
           \    /\
            \  /
             \/
            Helena
```

It's not a love triangle, it's a love rectangle, with everyone in love with someone who doesn't love him or her back **(Act II, Sc. 2).**

When Oberon finds out what has happened, he's furious at Puck, but Puck just finds the whole thing hysterical! Still, Puck goes off to find Helena while Oberon charms the eyes of Demetrius **(Act III, Sc. 2).** When this lover wakes up, he falls in love with Helena just like Lysander, who has been following her around like a puppy. The situation is now exactly the opposite of the way it was at the beginning of the play, and looks like this:

```
           Hermia
            /
           /
          V
     Lysander   Demetrius
          \    /\
           \  //
            \//
           Helena
```

One would think that the one person who would be happy

about all this would be Helena, who has gone from being entirely unloved to being adored by two men. But she's convinced that they're only making fun of her (today we might say she has a self-esteem problem). The more they say they love her, the more miserable she becomes. When Hermia

appears, after chasing through the forest seeking her missing Lysander, Helena finally thinks she has figured out what is going on. Hermia, her oldest, dearest friend, must have sent both of her lovers to make fun of her. Meanwhile, Hermia sees Lysander mooning over her best friend, and naturally concludes that Helena has stolen him away. We find out that Hermia is fairly short: when the other

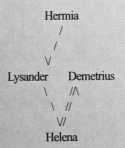

Sources

Shakespeare borrowed many of the plots of his plays, though he always skillfully adapted and often improved them. *Hamlet*, for instance, was an old story that had been made into a fairly successful play during Shakespeare's lifetime, though of course he sharpened the themes and added his own language.

As far as we know, there's no single source for *Midsummer Night's Dream*. The fairies seem to come largely from folklore and Shakespeare's own imagination, perhaps inspired by a speech he had written earlier for *Romeo and Juliet*:

> Oh, then I see Queen Mab has been with you.
> She is the fairies' midwife, and she comes
> In shape no bigger than an agate stone

On the forefinger of an alderman
Drawn by a team of little atomies
Athwart men's noses as they lie asleep.
(Act I, Sc. 4)

Critics have also attempted to tie the play to various other sources relating to myths of Diana, the legend of Theseus, and various stories about competing lovers.

The part of the play for which he drew most heavily on outside material was the story of Pyramus and Thisbe, which he used for the rustics' play-within-a-play. There were many versions of this story, some old and some quite recent to Shakespeare's time. None of the others who used the story, though, saw its ridiculous side the way Shakespeare did!

---

characters join to make fun of her, calling her a "bead, acorn, minimus," she retaliates by calling Helena a "painted maypole" **(Act III, Sc. 2)**.

What follows is pure chaos.

PUPPET? AY, THAT WAY GOES THE GAME. WITH HER HEIGHT, SHE HATH PREVAIL'D WITH HIM. HOW LOW AM I, THOU PAINTED MAYPOLE? NOT SO LOW BUT THAT MY NAILS CAN REACH INTO THINE EYES.

Hermia is trying to attack Helena, Helena is trying to get away, and the two men are fighting each other for Helena's attention. The scene is often staged with characters running around, waving swords, hiding behind trees, and grabbing each others' feet. It's one of the most active scenes in Shakespeare. It's also a formula which Shakespeare had used before and would use again in his comedies: a complicated situation, in which some or all of the participants are oblivious to some crucial fact which we, the audience, know.

Eventually, Oberon straightens everything out. First he has Puck create a fog and turn invisible, imitating the voices of the two men to lure them apart so they don't injure one another. Then he puts all four lovers to sleep. Finally, he puts the juice from another flower on Lysander's eyes, curing the earlier love spell. When the lovers finally wake up, everything is the way it should be: Lysander and Hermia in love, as they were at the beginning, and Demetrius loving Helena. Best of all, they can remember almost nothing of the passions, disappointments and quarrels of the previous night, and what they can remember seems to be nothing but a fading dream.

Demetrius no longer wishes to marry Hermia, so her father Egeus has no more power over her, and all four lovers go back into the city to be married. Of course, Demetrius is still under the influence of the love-spell when he marries Helena, but presumably they'll both live happily ever after just the same.

MOONLIGHT AND THE IMAGINATION

In the BBC production of this play, which isn't too difficult to find on video, in Act I all the characters are dressed in stiff, formal Elizabethan garb, with wide collars and elegant hairdos. The blocking of the scenes is stiff and formal, and the characters seem almost locked inside their uncomfortable outfits. Even the tradesmen-actors, holding their meeting inside a pub, are all neatly lined up on a bench, with little movement or action.

The turning point of the play comes at the beginning of Act II, when we move out of the confining daytime world of the city into the ever-shifting, liberating, nighttime world of the forest. The BBC version opens this scene with Puck cavorting through a moonlit pool and splashing water on another fairy. Water is a frequently-used symbol of this unstable kingdom, where everything is only a reflection of its true shape, and can break apart and re-form at any moment. The moon is another major symbol, for it has many different shapes and forms; as "governess of floods" **(Act II, Sc. 1)** it draws the tide and, as Renaissance scientists believed, the dew as well. This is the realm ruled over by Titania, which is another name for Diana, the moon goddess. By the end of the Act IV in the BBC production, the lovers have lost all their stiffness and dignity and most of their clothes, and are falling into the pond in their nightshirts, soaked and covered with mud, with no restrictions and nothing holding them back either physically or emotionally.

We can't really trust our senses in the moonlit forest. Indeed, sensual displacement, or synesthesia, is another theme of the play. When Bottom wakes up and tries to remember what has happened to him, he can't tell one sense from

I HAVE HAD A DREAM -- THE EYE OF MAN HATH NOT HEARD, THE EAR OF MAN HATH NOT SEEN, MAN'S HAND IS NOT ABLE TO TASTE, NOR HIS HEART TO REPORT WHAT MY DREAM WAS. I WILL GET PETER QUINCE TO WRITE A BALLAD. IT SHALL BE CALLED "BOTTOM'S DREAM," BECAUSE IT HATH NO BOTTOM.

another: "The eye of man hath not heard, the ear of man hath not seen, man's hand is not able to taste, his tongue to conceive, nor his heart to report, what my dream was" **(Act IV, Sc. 1).**

When the lovers and the rustics leave the safety of the daytime city and go into the mysterious night-time forest, they leave behind the safe confines of reality in exchange for a world full of mystery, illusion, and dreams. The fairies, with their invisibility and transformations, are one manifestation of this dreamlike state, but Shakespeare is also suggesting, slyly, that love itself may be yet another sort of delusion.

One of the most important speeches of the play, which explains its major theme rather neatly, belongs to Duke Theseus in Act IV. The lovers have just returned from the forest in the morning, bringing with them their rather confused and incoherent account of the night's adventures. Hippolyta, betrothed to Theseus, asks him what he thinks of their story. Theseus responds with this famous speech:

> *I never may believe*
> *These antick fables, nor these fairy*
> *toys.*
> *Lovers and madmen have such*
> *seething brains,*
> *Such shaping fantasies, that appre*
> *hend*
> *More than cool reason ever compre*
> *hends.*
> *The lunatic, the lover, and the poet,*
> *Are of imagination all compact:*
> *One sees more devils than vast hell*
> *can hold,*
> *That is the madman; the lover, all*
> *as frantic,*
> *Sees Helen's beauty in a brow*
> *of Egypt:*
> *The poet's eye, in a fine frenzy*
> *rolling,*
> *Doth glance from heaven to earth,*
> *from earth to heaven;*
> *And, as imagination bodies forth*
> *The forms of things unknown, the*
> *poet's pen*
> *Turns them to shapes, and gives to*
> *airy nothing*
> *A local habitation and a name.*
> *Such tricks hath strong imagination,*
> *That, if it would but apprehend*
> *some joy,*
> *It comprehends some bringer of*
> *that joy;*
> *Or in the night, imagining some*
> *fear,*
> *How easy is a bush supposed a*
> *bear!*

(Act V, Sc. 1)

In the midst of a play filled with magic and fairies, Theseus remains the skeptic, dedicated to "cool reason." In his dismissal of all things having to do with the imagination, however, he classifies them into three categories: the lunatic, the lover, and the poet. It's a good idea to look at the different parts of this speech carefully.

The Lunatic

The first person that Theseus talks about is the madman. Along with its effect on water, the moon was thought by Renaissance philosophers to have an influence on the human brain. In fact, many people believe this even today, though it has been disproved by scientists. The word lunatic means, literally, "touched by the moon." The lunatic is at home in the lunar world of the forest, because he uses his imagination to create illusions—devils, fairies, or whatever.

The Lover

Lovers, Theseus argues, are just as deluded as madmen. Hermia's father Egeus goes so far as to say that his daughter has been bewitched by Lysander, and that sounds like a good description of the way love works in the play. If you are in love, you can look at someone whom everyone else agrees is ugly—the "brow of Egypt" (the Renaissance was prejudiced against dark complexions)—and consider her to be as beautiful as Helen of Troy. Where does the beauty come from? It's created from nothing by the mind of the lover, just as the mind of the madman creates demons.

Today we say that beauty is in the eye of the beholder, and with Oberon's flower that figure of speech becomes literal. The many references to eyes in the play would have had great significance in the Renaissance: philosophers at the time thought that, when you saw something, you actually created a sort of mirror image of that object inside your eye. When you fell in love, they wondered, were you falling in love with the person, or with the image you had created? In Merchant of Venice, Shakespeare wrote

> Tell me where is fancy bred,
> Or in the heart or in the head?
> How begot, how nourished?
> Reply, reply.
> It is engendered in the eyes,
> With gazing fed; and fancy dies
> In the cradle where it lies.
> **(Act III, Sc. 2)**

THEY ALL LEAVE THE PALACE EXCEPT HERMIA AND LYSANDER . . .

THE COURSE OF TRUE LOVE NEVER DID RUN SMOOTH.

O, TO CHOOSE LOVE BY ANOTHER'S EYES!

When Hermia is trying to win Theseus to her cause, she complains, "I would my father looked but with my eyes," to which the Duke replies "Rather your eyes must with his judgement look" **(Act I, Sc. 1).**

Many people looking at the play have noticed that there doesn't seem to be a whole lot of difference between the four lovers. Hermia is shorter than Helena, Demetrius is perhaps not quite as nice as Lysander, but overall, there doesn't seem to be much to choose between them. Lysander himself complains that his family and wealth are identical to those of Demetrius:

> *I am, my lord, as well derived as he,*
> *As well possess'd; my love is more than his;*
> *My fortunes every way as fairly rank'd,*
> *If not with vantage, as Demetrius.*
> **(Act I, Sc. 1)**

The terms of endearment that the men use when they are bewitched to be in love with Helena sound just the same as the vows they made to Hermia. Shakespeare seems to be saying that, since love is something that comes from within your mind, it doesn't really matter whom you fall in love with, as long as the love is returned. It's almost as if Oberon just keeps rolling the dice until he comes up with two pairs.

The Poet

The third type of lunatic that Theseus talks about is the poet. The irony, of course, is that Shakespeare himself is a poet, so he's really writing about himself. Like the lover and the madman, the poet creates something out of nothing. The poet, however, does more than either of the other two, for he can bring the things that he imagines out of his mind and into the real world, giving "to airy nothing / A local habitation and a name." He can even make us believe, if only for a moment, that the woods might be filled with fairies, and a man might be given a donkey's head.

But the poet's imagination cannot work alone. He requires the imagination of the audience as well, to bring his dreams to life. This act on the part of the audience is sometimes called "suspension of disbelief." We know that there are no such things as fairies, but while we are watching the play, we agree to pretend that there are. If we don't make this bargain with the playwright, our enjoyment of the play is greatly diminished.

IF YOU SHOULD DO IT TOO TERRIBLY, YOU WOULD FRIGHTEN THE DUCHESS AND THE LADIES THAT THEY WOULD SHRIEK; AND THAT WERE ENOUGH TO HANG US ALL.

In Peter Quince's theatrical company we see poets (to use the term loosely) who don't realize that the theater is a mixture of what is real and what the audience agrees to believe. As far as the rustics are concerned, anything that is on stage is really happening; they're like yokels who run from a movie theater when a monster appears on screen. The rustics are afraid that, if Snug the joiner shows up on stage dressed as a lion, all the ladies in the audience will be terrified by the ferocious beast and the Duke will have them all hanged.

To prevent this, they write a Prologue in which the lion explains that he is no lion, but rather Snug the joiner. Likewise, they are temporarily baffled as to how to show to the audience that the lovers are meeting at night, so they come up with the idea of dressing up one of their number as the moon, and have him explain that it's nighttime. (This is another of the many guises in which the moon appears in the play.)

Of course, as a playwright Shakespeare was confronted with this sort of problem all the time. He had little in terms of special effects or scenery to help him create an illusion. There was no special lighting; everything took place in the broad light of midday. When he had to describe something spectacular, he knew that he would have to make it happen, not on-stage, but within the audience's minds. This is how he does it in *Henry V*, when he needs to have us imagine a great army setting sail across the sea:

> *Thus with imagined wing our*
> *swift Scene flies*
> *In motion of no less celerity*
> *Than that of thought. Suppose that*
> *you have seen*
> *The well-appointed king of*
> *Hampton   pier*
> *Embark his royalty; and his brave*
> *fleet...*
> *Play with your fancies, and in them*
> *behold*
> *Upon the hempen tackle ship-boys*
> *climbing....*
> *Grapple your minds to sternage of*
> *this navy,*
> *And leave your England....*
> *Work, work your thoughts, and*
> *therein see a siege....*
> *Still be kind,*
> *And eke out our performance with*
> *your mind.*
> **(Henry V -Act III. Sc. 1)**

A Midsummer Night's Dream is almost like a series of lessons, training us on how to use our imaginations to be a good audience. Skeptic though he is, Duke Theseus remembers this crucial part of drama. When his bride Hippolyta complains of the rustics' performance that, " This is the silliest stuff that e'er I heard," he responds,

"The best in this kind are but shadows, and the worst are no worse, if imagination amend them." Hippolyta responds with a statement true for all theatrical productions: "It must be your imagination then, and not theirs" **(Act V, Sc. 1)**. And at the very end of the play, Puck reminds us that nothing has happened that has not taken place within our own minds:

> *If we shadows have offended,*
> *Think but this, and all is mended,*
> *That you have but slumber'd here*
> *While these visions did appear.*
> *And this weak and idle theme,*
> *No more yielding but a dream,*
> *Gentles, do not reprehend:*
> *If you pardon, we will mend.*
> *And, as I am an honest Puck,*
> *If we have unearned luck*
> *Now to 'scape the serpent's tongue,*
> *We will make amends ere long;*
> *Else the Puck a liar call:*
> *So, good night unto you all.*
> *Give me your hands, if we be friends,*
> *And Robin shall restore amends.*
>
> **(p. 44; Act V, Sc. 1)**

like to catch the ferry across the Thames to watch one of Shakespeare's plays.

•Is Shakespeare sympathetic to the rustics, or is he simply making fun of them?

•Hermia, Helena, Demetrius, and Lysander are all relatively miserable for most of the play. Despite this fact, or perhaps because of it, we find their behavior funny. Is this only because we know everything will work out in the end, or are we always cheered up by remembering that some people are worse off than we are?

•What do you think makes people fall in love? Does the idea of Puck wandering around with a magic flower in his hand make any more or less sense than any other explanation?

Discussion Questions

•What qualities would you expect to find in a "great writer?" What kind of childhood and education would you expect such a person to have had?

•Find out about the Globe Theatre and write about what you imagine it would be

About the Essayist:

Bruce Glassco is an Assistant Professor of English at Mt. Senario College in Ladysmith, Wisconsin. He holds an M.A. and Ph.D. from the University of Virginia, and attended the Clarion Writers' Workshop in 1995. He has directed a number of productions, including *A Midsummer Night's Dream*.